Illustrated by

Stik

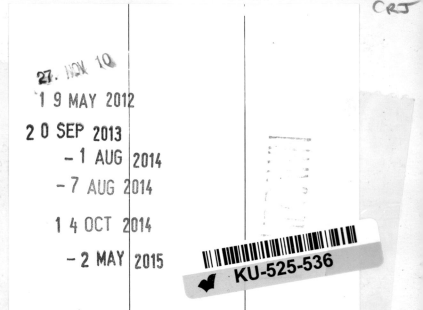

Rising Stars UK Ltd.
22 Grafton Street, London W1S 4EX
www.risingstars-uk.com

The right of Roger Hurn to be identified as the author of this work
has been asserted by him in accordance with the Copyright,
Design and Patents Act 1988.

Published 2008

Cover design: Burville-Riley Partnership
Illustrator: Stik, Bill Greenhead for Illustration Ltd
Text design and typesetting: Andy Wilson
Publisher: Gill Budgell
Editor: Catherine Baker

British Library Cataloguing in Publication Data.
A CIP record for this book is available from the British Library

ISBN: 978-1-84680-432-8

Printed in the UK by CPI Bookmarque, Croydon, CR0 4TD

Mixed Sources
Product group from well-managed
forests and other controlled sources
www.fsc.org Cert no. TT-COC-002227
© 1996 Forest Stewardship Council
FSC

Contents

Meet the Mystery Mob

Name:

FYI: Gummy hasn't got much brain – and even fewer teeth.

Loves: Soup.

Hates: Toffee chews.

Fact: The brightest thing about him is his shirt.

Name:

Lee

FYI: If Lee was any cooler he'd be a cucumber.

Loves: Hip-hop.

Hates: Hopscotch.

Fact: He has his own designer label (which he peeled off a tin).

Name:

Rob

FYI: Rob lives in his own world – he's just visiting planet Earth.

Loves: Daydreaming.

Hates: Nightmares.

Fact: Rob always does his homework – he just forgets to write it down.

Name:

Dwayne

FYI: Dwayne is smarter than a tree full of owls.

Loves: Anything complicated.

Hates: Join-the-dots books.

Fact: If he was any brighter you could use him as a floodlight at football matches.

Name:

Chet

FYI: Chet is as brave as a lion with steel jaws.

Loves: Having adventures.

Hates: Knitting.

Fact: He's as tough as the chicken his granny cooks for his tea.

Name:

Adi

FYI: Adi is as happy as a football fan with tickets to the big match.

Loves: Telling jokes.

Hates: Moaning minnies.

Fact: He knows more jokes than a jumbo joke book.

Monster's Mansion

The Mystery Mob are big fans
of the TV show *Monster's Mansion*.
It's filmed at the home of
Plenty O'Dosh, the world's
richest woman. On the programme,
kids who have made awesome
inventions show them to Plenty
O'Dosh. Then she chooses
the best one and puts it on sale
in all the big stores – and the kid
who invented it gets a big fat cheque!

Gummy   Wow, this is such a cool show. But why's it called *Monster's Mansion*?

Dwayne   Because Plenty O'Dosh lives in a big house and she's got a monster amount of money to give away.

Gummy   So she's not really a monster then?

Dwayne No, but she scares me.

Gummy Why?

Dwayne Because she's meaner than
a T-Rex with toothache if she
doesn't like your invention.

This doesn't worry the Mob. They want
to go on the show. They work hard
on their inventions, but in the end
only Dwayne and Gummy's invention
is good enough to have a chance
of making it on to the show.

Gummy   I liked Rob and Lee's
            inflatable dartboard.

Dwayne   Yes. It was just a shame that it
            burst when that dart hit it.

Gummy   Hmmm. Maybe they needed
            to invent rubber-tipped darts
            to go with it.

Dwayne   But they'd just bounce off
            the dartboard.

Gummy   Exactly!

Dwayne   Doh! Gummy, you're the kind
of person who'd sit on the ejector
seat in a helicopter if it had one.

Gummy   Huh. I know you think I'm dim,
but I'm not. I'd only sit on it
if I was wearing a parachute.

Dwayne   (sighing) Good thinking, Gum.

Gummy   Hey, Chet and Adi's silent alarm
clock was an awesome idea.

Dwayne   Yes, but only for people
who don't like getting up
in the morning.

Gummy   Yeah. That's why I liked it.

Buster,
the Chore-busting Robot

Dwayne and Gummy's invention is
Buster, the chore-busting robot.
It does all the household chores
that everyone hates to do.
They take Buster to try out
for the show. The robot wows
the director of *Monster's Mansion*.

TV Director

Okay, guys. That robot is wicked.
You are definitely going to be
on the show.

Gummy   Wow! Does that mean we'll get
to meet Plenty O'Dosh?

TV Director

It sure does. But watch out, boys.
Her bite is worse than her bark.

Gummy   Did you hear that, Dwayne?
I guess she really is a monster
after all.

The TV guy chuckles and walks away. The rest of the Mystery Mob high five Dwayne and Gummy. But some of the other inventors are not so happy. Buster the robot is just too good.

Dwayne Hey, Gum! It's sooo cool that we're on the show. But that's not the best bit.

Gummy So what's the best bit?

Dwayne We only get to stay in
Plenty O'Dosh's mansion
while the show's being made!

Gummy You're kidding me!

Dwayne No kidding. So come on –
let's grab Buster and pack
our bags!

It's the day before the show,
and all the contestants are
arriving at the mansion.

Gummy   Wow! Just look at the size
of this place!

Dwayne   Yeah. Plenty certainly lives
up to her name – she's got loads
of dosh.

Gummy   Never mind the dosh – I just hope
she's got loads of nosh.
I'm starving!

Dwayne Doh! You and your stomach!
Come on then – let's put Buster
in our room and go and find
something to eat.

The boys leave Buster in the room
and head off in search of food –
but they forget to lock the door.
When they come back to check on
Buster, they get a nasty shock!

Dwayne Oh no! Buster's not here.

Gummy Maybe he's hiding from us.

Dwayne No way. I switched him off.

Gummy So where is he, then?

Dwayne I don't know, but I'd say
someone has stolen him!
And we can't make another
robot for the show.
There just isn't time.

Gummy So what can we do?

Dwayne   We've got to
find the thief
and get Buster back.

Gummy   (eagerly) Brilliant idea, Dwayne!
Er ... but the thief hasn't left
a single clue behind.

Dwayne   There's only one thing for it.
We'll just have to search
everywhere.

But even though the boys hunt
high and low, there is no sign of
the missing robot. This is bad news.
Without Buster, there is no way
Dwayne and Gummy can take part
in the *Monster's Mansion* TV show.

Barbecued Chicken

The next morning, Dwayne and Gummy get a big surprise. Buster the robot has reappeared in their room!

Gummy Buster – you're back!

Dwayne The question is: how did he get here?

Gummy Maybe he escaped.

Dwayne   Hmmm … maybe. But we
don't have time to worry about it.
The main thing is we can still
be on the show if we hurry.

Gummy   You're right. Let's go.

The boys make it just in time.
They race in with Buster. Plenty O'Dosh
is sitting in her chair watching them.

Dwayne This is Buster, the chore-busting robot.

Gummy We invented him.
He does the jobs you hate.

Dwayne That's right, Ms O'Dosh.
When I press the buttons
on this control pad, Buster
will put the dishes on the table
while cooking a hot meal in
the microwave oven in his chest.

Plenty Hmmm … that sounds good.
I hate cooking dinner.
Okay, put Buster to work.

Dwayne presses the buttons on the pad.
Buster opens a metal flap in his chest
and puts a chicken dinner inside.
But then he goes crazy and starts
smashing all the dishes!

Gummy He's out of control.
Stop him Dwayne. Quick!

Dwayne It's no good. I'm pressing
the buttons, but he isn't taking
any notice.

Gummy Oh, it's okay. He's stopped now.

Dwayne Yes, but that's only because he's smashed all the dishes.

Gummy Never mind, maybe he's still cooked the dinner.

Dwayne Well, don't just stand there, go and see.

Gummy runs over to the robot.
He opens the flap and takes out
the dinner. It's ruined.

Gummy   Er … the chicken's a tiny bit flame-grilled.

Plenty   No it isn't! It's burnt to a cinder! I can't eat that.

Dwayne   (sadly) Well, we haven't got any dishes left for you to eat it off anyway.

Gummy   (brightly) And there's more good news, Ms O'Dosh! Now Buster's smashed the dishes, you don't have to worry about doing the washing up.

Plenty You two are about as much use as non-stick sellotape. Get out – and take your rotten robot with you!

Dwayne and Gummy walk off. They're fed up. They just can't figure out why Buster flipped.

4

Robot Control

Next up on the show is a girl inventor
called Anita. She has a robot too.
It looks just like Buster.

Gummy Hey, that's Buster! What's he
doing with that girl?

Dwayne She must be the thief! She's made
an evil lookalike of Buster,
then switched the two of them
over. We've got the wrong robot!

Gummy   Oh no! Her robot's fantastic.
It's doing all the chores.
Plenty O'Dosh looks really
impressed. She'll give that cheat
the cheque for sure.

Dwayne   Grrrr! There must be something
we can do.

Gummy   We can tell Ms O'Dosh the truth
about what's happened.

Dwayne   No, she'll never believe us.
We'll just sound like bad losers.

Gummy   So what are we going to do?

Dwayne   I don't know, Gum, but we're not beaten yet. Just let me put my thinking cap on.

Gummy   Is that like some kind of baseball cap?

Dwayne   (wearily) Yes, but it's invisible.

Gummy   Ah, that explains why I've never seen you wearing it before.

Dwayne stares at Anita and the real Buster. Then he smiles and snaps his fingers.

Dwayne Hey, I've still got Buster's remote control pad. I had it in my pocket when Anita stole him.

Gummy Do you think it will still work on him?

Dwayne Well, there's only one way to find out!

Dwayne points the remote control pad at Buster and presses the buttons. Gummy holds his breath.

All Washed Up

Buster has a plate of fried eggs and baked beans in his hands, and he's about to serve it to Plenty O'Dosh. Suddenly he tips it on to her lap.

Gummy   Yes! Way to go, Buster.

Dwayne   You ain't seen nothing yet, Gummy. Watch this. Buster's putting a chip up her nose and a sausage in each of her ears!

Gummy All right! Hey, Ms O'Dosh isn't looking so happy with Anita now.

Dwayne Okay. Let's go and see if we can't get Anita to admit she switched robots.

Gummy She'll never do that.

Dwayne Oh, I think she will ... when she sees what I've got planned for her.

Dwayne and Gummy run back out
in front of the TV cameras.

Plenty   What are you two doing here?

Gummy   We've come to make Anita
'fess up that she's a cheat.

Dwayne   That's right. Come on, Anita,
you switched Buster for your
robot because you knew if we
had the evil robot we'd lose.

Anita   I'm admitting nothing.

Gummy   Oh well, fair enough.
        At least we tried.

Dwayne No, Gum, we're not giving up
        that easily.

Gummy   But what can we do?

Dwayne Plenty. Okay, Anita, do you see
        that huge bowl of jelly trifle?

Anita   Yeah. What are you going to do
        with it?

Gummy   We're going to eat it.

Dwayne No, we're not. Buster is
        going to dump it
        all over you
        unless you
        tell the truth.

The robot picks up the bowl and holds it over Anita's head.

Anita   No – wait! I confess! I switched the robots. Just don't tip that stuff on me. I really hate jelly trifle.

Dwayne Okay. I won't. Whoops! My finger's slipped. Sorry.

Dwayne pushes the button and Buster drops the bowl on Anita. She is covered from head to toe in sloppy trifle.

Anita   Eurgghhh! Yuk!

Plenty   Somebody get that cheat
out of here! And who's going
to clean this mess off me?

Gummy   No problem, Ms O'Dosh.

Dwayne   Buster will fix it.

The security guards take Anita away
while Buster gives Plenty O'Dosh
a quick makeover. She soon looks
as good as new.

Plenty   Fetch me my cheque book.
You two boys have won.
Your robot is the best!

Dwayne and Gummy give each other
high fives. They are delighted.
The end credits roll.
Dwayne reads them
and slaps his head.

Dwayne Doh! We should have guessed that Anita was the thief.

Gummy How?

Dwayne Well, her full name is Anita Steel.

Gummy So?

Dwayne So that makes her 'I need ta steal', geddit?

The boys laugh all the way to the bank.

About the author

Roger Hurn has:

 had a hit record in Turkey

won *The Weakest Link* on TV

swum with sharks on the
Great Barrier Reef.

Now he's a writer, and he hopes you like
reading about the Mystery Mob as much as he
likes writing about them.

Inventions quiz

Questions

1 Why did the inventor put dynamite
   in his fridge?

2 What kind of invention is moontan lotion?

3 Who invented fire?

4 What do you call the inventor
   who invented the Fast Food Diet?

5 What did the kindly inventor make
   for the short-sighted ghost?

6 An inventor invented a clock that had
   fangs and yelled at people. What did he
   call it?

7 Who invented fractions?

8 What did the inventor invent
   to take with him in the desert?

Answers

1 Because he wanted to blow his cool.
2 A very silly one.
3 Some bright spark!
4 Very, very rich!
5 A pair of spooktacles.
6 An alarming clock.
7 Henry the 1/8.
8 A thirst-aid kit.

How did you score?

✋ If you got all eight inventions quiz answers correct, then you are very inventive indeed!

✋ If you got six inventions quiz answers correct, then you are an apprentice inventor.

✋ If you got fewer than four inventions quiz answers correct, then you're the kind of inventor who'd invent an umbrella that dissolves when wet.

When I was a kid

Question When you were a kid, did you ever invent anything?

Roger Yes, I invented lots of things.

Question Like what?

Roger Well, first up I invented a broom with a bent handle for sweeping round corners.

Question Anything else?

Roger Yes. Then I invented a cat flap for the fridge.

Question Didn't that make your mum really cross?

Roger Yes, she was too big to squeeze through it. But the cat thought it was great.

Adi's favourite inventor joke

Did you hear about the inventor who invented a gas that can burn through anything?

Yes, now he's trying to invent something to keep it in.

Five fantastically silly inventions

 Have you ever tried to stay awake to see Father Christmas on Christmas Eve, but fell asleep before he arrived? Well, you need the 'Santa Claus Detector' (invented 1996). Just hang the detector over the fireplace and when Santa comes down the chimney the lights on the detector start flashing. (You could be in for a long wait.)

 Do your teachers give you enough praise? If not, just use the 'Pat On the Back Apparatus' (invented 1986). It's a plastic hand on a stick. Use it and it's sure to make you feel better about yourself – not!

If you like roller skating, but are too lazy to keep taking your shoes on and off, just get some 'knee skates' (invented 1998). Strap them on to your knees and off you go. When you've finished skating just stand up and walk away. Perfect!

 Do you wish you had fancy gadgets like James Bond? Well, get yourself the 'Flying Saucer Submarine' (invented 1997) and James Bond will envy you! Unfortunately, it doesn't actually work – yet.

Have you ever gone to the toilet in the middle of the night when it was too dark to see what you were doing? Ugh! But with the 'Toilet Landing Lights' (invented 1993) you'll never have to worry about missing the loo ever again.

How to be an inventor

1 Wear a hat with a light bulb on top of it so people will think you're having a bright idea.

2 Never take any notice when people tell you your ideas are mad. But if you want to invent things like glow-in-the-dark sunglasses, you probably are.

3 If at first you don't succeed with your invention, try and try again. But if you still haven't succeeded after that then they are probably right – your ideas are mad!

4 Never try to invent anything that needs gunpowder and matches to make it work.

5 Always try to invent something useful. Here are five things you really don't want to invent: a solar-powered torch; waterproof teabags; an inflatable anchor; an unsinkable submarine; sugar-coated toothpaste.

Inventor lingo

Invention Something an inventor makes that no one else has thought of. For example, a concrete kite. No one has thought of making that ...

Inventor A person who invents things. Leonardo da Vinci was the world's greatest inventor. He thought of inventing parachutes long before there were any aeroplanes. How weird is that?

Nuts Not a tasty snack, but what most inventors get called at some point in their career.

Patent The agreement that gives the inventor the right to stop anyone using his invention without his say so. Mind you, even if someone invented them, would you really want to wear cement swimming trunks?

Robot Science-fiction writer Karel Capek was the first person to think up the word 'robot'. He wrote about them in his book, *War with the Newts*! Now that does sound like a weird book.

Mystery Mob

Mystery Mob Set 1:

Mystery Mob and the Abominable Snowman
Mystery Mob and the Big Match
Mystery Mob and the Circus of Doom
Mystery Mob and the Creepy Castle
Mystery Mob and the Haunted Attic
Mystery Mob and the Hidden Treasure
Mystery Mob and the Magic Bottle
Mystery Mob and the Missing Millions
Mystery Mob and the Monster on the Moor
Mystery Mob and the Mummy's Curse
Mystery Mob and the Time Machine
Mystery Mob and the UFO

Mystery Mob Set 2:

Mystery Mob and the Ghost Town
Mystery Mob and the Bonfire Night Plot
Mystery Mob and the April Fools' Day Joker
Mystery Mob and the Great Pancake Day Race
Mystery Mob and the Scary Santa
Mystery Mob and the Conker Conspiracy
Mystery Mob and the Top Talent Contest
Mystery Mob and the Night in the Waxworks
Mystery Mob and the Runaway Train
Mystery Mob and the Wrong Robot
Mystery Mob and the Day of the Dinosaurs
Mystery Mob and the Man-eating Tiger

RISING ★ STARS

Mystery Mob books are available from most booksellers.

**For mail order information
please call Rising Stars on 0871 47 23 010
or visit www.risingstars-uk.com**